CREATURES

in an

ALPHABET

by Djuna Barnes

The Book of Repulsive Women
A Book
Ladies Almanack
A Night Among the Horses
Ryder
Nightwood
Spillway
The Antiphon

Djuna Barnes

CREATURES

in an

ALPHABET

The Dial Press

New York

Published by
The Dial Press
1 Dag Hammarskjold Plaza
New York, New York 10017

Grateful acknowledgment is made for permission
to reproduce art from the Kubler Collection,
Cooper-Hewitt Museum Library Picture Collection,
Smithsonian Institution, New York;
The New York Public Library; and
Walters Art Gallery, Baltimore

Manufactured in the United States of America
First printing
Design by Francesca Belanger
Art research by Linda Gutierrez

Library of Congress Cataloging in Publication Data
Barnes, Djuna.
Creatures in an alphabet.
1. Animals—Poetry. 2. Alphabet rhymes. I. Title.
PS3503.A614C7   811'.52   82-5086
ISBN 0-385-27797-0   AACR2

For Emily Coleman

The adder in the grass can hiss
The lynxes in the dark can kiss
Each otter holds his otter's hand
For this is how the Lord has planned.

Alas!

When hovering, the Hummingbird
Is always going home (it's said).
By flying in a single spot
It's striving fast to think it's not.

Why is it the Donkey haws,
And backs away (the mule) because
Although it hasn't said it's who,
It's practicing *solfeggio.*

The reason that the Elephant
Is both detained and yet at ease,
Is because it is four trees
That the Lord forgot to plant.

With cloven lip, with baleful eye,
The Camel wears the caliph high.
But though he do the master's will,
He himself's his habit still.

The Fish, the Fish, how is he caught?
With grave intent, or so we thought;
Yet with what a flattened look
It goes fishing, without hook.

The trim Giraffe, on ankles slight,
Dips its crown in pale moonlight;
But what it poles for, none can say—
It's much too up and high away.

The Hippo is a wading junk,
A sort of Saratoga trunk
With all its trappings on its back,
Through which the birds of passage peck.

When from mischief interdict,
The Imago perfected rise,
And lays its dool at Heaven's Gate,
Then in this alphabet it is.

Though it be loud with auguries
Of summer sun, and happy days;
Nonetheless the Blue Jay is
Lined with insect agonies.

The Kinkajou, the hanging sloth,
Or any else that looks uncouth,
Aren't they somewhat upside down?
Or are they merely three of both?

Horrid hunger is the cause,
That opens up the Lion's jaws;
Yet what it tears apart for meat
Is merely what its victims ate.

In the zoo the Monkeys screech
At any dainty out of reach;
Yet let a corpulence be found,
They whack it madly to the ground.

If ascension is your hope,
Ride not the Nigor (antelope)
But mount the springbok for the run;
It jumps straight up, like hot popcorn.

When musing on the Ocelot,
Or on the panther's hurling tail,
One wonders how such stealth is caught,
And how it be the cats prevail.

If among itself it go,
(As the Peacock's said to do),
With all its thousand eyes ajar,
Is it itself it's looking for?

Now for quidnunc, now for Quail,
(One runs off, the others rail);
But what about? It ends the same—
An old man's titter, a young man's game.

What of Raccoon, animal?
With visor down (or domino),
When at *ombre* or *quadrille,*
Will it vail and let you know?

The Seal, she lounges like a bride,
Much too docile, there's no doubt;
Madame Récamier, on side,
(If such she has), and bottom out.

"Tyger! Tyger!"—Who wrote that?
You won't take it with your hat,
Nor lure it with a golden cage;
It won't leap its master's page.

Unicorn, the one-horned beast
Mistranslated from the start,
(See Deuteronomy, at least),
An upright, but a much vex'd art.

Now of the Vesper Wasp beware,
Its butt and bust hang by an hair,
Its sting's a death; otherwise
It's riggish in its enterprise.

Somewhat sullen, many days,
The Walrus is a cow that neighs.
Tusked, ungainly, and windblown,
It sits on ice, and alone.

As there was nothing more to say,
The X has crossed himself away.
And as there's nothing new to prove,
He marked his exit with his love.

A bale of hair, the Yak he be,
His bitter butter minged in tea;
With all his craggy services,
His lowly life Himalayan is.

('Round the mulberry we go.)

About the Author

Djuna Barnes was born June 12, 1892, on Storm King Mountain at Cornwall-on-Hudson, New York. Her parents were Wald Barnes (whose given name was Henry Budington) of Springfield, Massachusetts, and Elizabeth Chappell of Oakham, Rutlandshire, England. Her father was an author, painter, musician, and poet; he invented her name. His mother, Zadel Barnes, had a literary salon in Grosvenor Square. Later, between them, they instructed his children. Although she never had a formal education, Miss Barnes studied art at Pratt Institute and at the Art Students League.

Miss Barnes began her career as a reporter, special-feature writer, and illustrator; starting with the *Brooklyn Eagle,* she wrote for nearly every newspaper in New York. Her short stories appeared in many magazines, from the famous racing sheet the *Morning Telegraph* to the *Dial, Smart Set, Vanity Fair,* and *The Little Review.*

Her first short stories to be printed in book form were gathered together with verse and drawings into a hardcover edition called *A Book.* Following that, her novel *Ryder* was published. On reaching best-seller lists, *Ryder* was followed by *A Night Among the Horses,* which is a reissue of *A Book* with added material. Then Miss Barnes left for Paris—with letters of introduction to James Joyce and Ezra Pound. In 1928 *Ladies Almanack* was privately printed in France.

In 1936 Faber & Faber of London issued (after its rejection in America) her now legendary novel *Nightwood*. Three of Miss Barnes's one-act plays were put on the Provincetown Playhouse's Macdougal Street stage; another play, *The Dove,* was produced at the Studio Theatre of Smith College. In 1961 her verse play *The Antiphon* was premiered at the Royal Theatre of Stockholm in the Dag Hammarskjöld–Gierow translation.

At first T. S. Eliot said he "hated" *The Antiphon,* though he later said to Miss Barnes that "It has the greatest last act I have ever read." The London *Times Literary Supplement* remarked, "It is probable that there always will be one or two eccentrics who think it gives its author the first place among women who have written first in the English language." Hammarskjöld called her work "Himalayan."

Her work has been translated into many languages and extensively anthologized. She was a member of the National Institute of Arts and Letters, and in 1981 received a senior fellowship from the National Endowment for the Arts. Miss Barnes strongly influenced other important authors, including Malcolm Lowry, John Hawkes, and William Faulkner.

Miss Barnes lived for many years in seclusion in Greenwich Village, where she died June 18, 1982, at the age of ninety. She had been at work on the poems in this collection since the early sixties, along with many other verse projects. "Quarry," her epitaph, was printed in *The New Yorker* in 1969.